0 to 10

by Bobby Lynn Maslen
pictures by John R. Maslen

Scholastic Inc.
New York • Toronto • London • Auckland • Sydney • Mexico City • New Delhi • Hong Kong • Buenos Aires

Available Bob Books®:

Set 1: Beginning Readers — With consistent new sounds added gradually, your new reader is gently introduced to all the letters of the alphabet. They can soon say, "I read the whole book!®"

Set 2: Advancing Beginners — The use of three-letter words and consistent vowel sounds in slightly longer stories build skill and confidence.

Set 3: Word Families — Consonant blends, endings and a few sight words advance reading skills while the use of word families keep reading manageable.

Set 4: Compound Words — Longer books and complex words engage young readers as proficiency advances.

Set 5: Long Vowels — Silent *e* and other vowel blends build young readers' vocabulary and aptitude.

Bob Books® Collections:

Collection 1 — Includes Set 1: Beginning Readers and part of Set 2: Advancing Beginners

Collection 2 — Includes part of Set 2: Advancing Beginners and Set 3: Word Families

Collection 3 — Includes Set 4: Compound Words and Set 5: Long Vowels

Ask for Bob Books at your local bookstore, or visit www.bobbooks.com.

ISBN 0-545-02687-3

6 5 4 3 2 1 7 8 9 10 11/0

Printed in China
This edition first printing, September 2007

Zed had 0 (zero) beds.

Too bad, Zed.
0 beds.

Pop had 1 top hat.

Pat had 2 fat cats.

Tom met 3 big cops.

Lil had 4 lolly-pops.

Ron saw 5 wet rats.

Pam saw 6 big hats.

Peg had 7 pet hogs.

Bet met 8 bad dogs.

Sox saw 9 red hens.

Ben met 10 big men.

Ten was at. . . . .

The End

List of 41 words in 0 to 10

Short Vowels

a	e	i	o	sight
at	bed	big	cop	hi
bad	Ben	Lil	dog	saw
cat	Bet		hog	the
fat	end		lolly-pop	to
had	hen		Pop	too
hat	men		Ron	was
pal	met		Sox	zero
Pam	Peg		Tom	
Pat	pet		top	
rat	red			
	ten			
	wet			
	Zed			

53 total words in *0 to 10*